5 TALES OF CH

For a complete list of Management Books 2000 titles
visit our web-site on http://www.mb2000.com

5 TALES OF CHANGE

how people have wrestled with
change, and won!

Anthony Greenfield

To Neil,

Best wishes

Anthony Greenfield

III.
2000

To Abigail, Felicity
and Jenni

First published in 2012 by Management Books 2000 Ltd
Forge House, Limes Road
Kemble, Cirencester
Gloucestershire, GL7 6AD, UK
Tel: 0044 (0) 1285 771441
Email: info@mb2000.com
Web: www.mb2000.com

British Library Cataloguing in Publication Data is available

ISBN 9781852526955

Acknowledgements

I would like to thank Howard Bentley who helped inspire some of these stories and Simon Payne for his feedback and ideas. Many thanks also to Susan Glicher, Pam Schwarz and Mary Farias for their input.

People and organisations
throughout the world
struggle with change.
These five short stories
illustrate why and how to
win through.

CONTENTS

1. BAKED BEANS

Saturday Morning

There was a buzz about the Food Bank. It was early on a wintry Saturday morning, and volunteers were already busy packing boxes of food. Bill Palmer was putting one can of baked beans into each Family Box, while other volunteers added cereal, canned fruit, bread, peanut butter and other items donated by retailers, restaurants and charities. Each box would help feed a family for a week.

As he got into a rhythm packing cans, Bill's mind drifted from one thought to another. He pictured his son sat at home chewing the end of his pen as he studied for next week's exams. He wondered where he could rent a wetsuit for his sponsored swim across Lake Windermere and just how cold the water would be in April, before imagining a plate of hot baked beans on toast. All the while, he tried not to think of work, but inevitably his mind was drawn to the events of the previous week and some unresolved problems that had been niggling away at him for several months.

Bill found work at the Food Bank therapeutic. He liked the camaraderie and got great satisfaction from the immediacy of the results achieved through physical labour. At the end of today's shift, there would be several pallets piled high with Family Food Boxes, shrink-wrapped and ready to be sent out to distribution centres around the city to be handed out to needy people over the coming week. Perhaps it was the stark contrast between the solid, visible results achieved at the Food Bank and the intangible outcomes he produced in his job at Ascent Insurance that brought his frustrations to mind.

Bill managed a team that developed new IT systems and maintained existing systems for Ascent. He was proud of his team; they were a bright and able bunch and, on the whole, he got on well with all of them. They were keen and hardworking, but they could be quite geeky; often in love with the technology, but not the best at handling the people who used the systems they built.

He could not fault his team's commitment, which made it doubly annoying that they were so under-appreciated by the rest of the organisation. They seemed to be treated as a necessary evil, like taxation or politics. Bill felt aggrieved on their behalf, but at a loss as to how to change things. He did not expect to be lifted shoulder high by other managers every time the team delivered a new application, but they could at least stop grumbling about their people having to 'spend time away from real work' learning how to get the most out of new systems.

Whilst Bill was ruminating on these concerns and placing cans of beans into boxes with a heavy heart, Dan Wilson, Head of Volunteering, came by and greeted him. Bill liked Dan and, so it seemed, did everyone else. He was tall, broad shouldered and softly spoken. People felt at ease in his presence, yet his steady strength and determination encouraged people to work hard to gain his approval.

Dan ran an induction session before every volunteer shift. Bill had heard him give the same talk before, but that morning he studied him particularly closely, looking for clues as to how he galvanised a group of sleepy volunteers into action early on a Saturday morning – and how he managed to keep them coming back for more.

"Good morning, I am Dan Wilson," Dan began the induction as usual, "Thank you all for coming. Do you know why you're here?" This brought on smiles and laughter as people contemplated exactly why they had ventured out of their beds so early. Some were new volunteers who needed to learn exactly what was expected of them, others, like Bill, were regulars who already knew the ropes.

"We're here to feed the poor and needy of Westkirk," continued Dan answering his own question with quiet authority. "We packed 210,000 kg of food last year. Our target this year is 250,000 kg." He then explained people's duties and set a target for that morning's shift of packing 150 Family Boxes. "Let's get started," he said, as he led people from the induction room to the main packing area.

By the end of the induction, Bill felt energised and eager to get to work. He also felt a bond with the team, even though most were strangers, and, best of all, he felt good about himself. No wonder everyone liked Dan; he embodied the ethos of the Food Bank.

"How are you today, Bill?" asked Dan catching Bill's eye. Something in Dan's tone and steady gaze made Bill feel that simply replying "Fine, thanks" was not going to be enough to satisfy him.

"Hmmm...I'm thinking too much about work," said Bill. "It's been a tricky week."

"Anything I can do?" asked Dan.

"You could start by telling me how you do it. How do you get us all working away so happily on our own time and with no pay? At my work there's no end of griping from people even though they're mostly very well-paid. What's your magic formula?"

"That sounds like an end-of-shift conversation," replied Dan wryly. "Let's sit down with a cup of tea and I'll try to help you any way I can. I'm guessing you know much of our 'magic formula' already." Dan turned his gaze towards the large blue banner hanging over the main door to the warehouse before saying, "I'll see you later. No slowing down on the beans!"

Bill got back to work, but now his attention was drawn to the blue banner, which read:

Our Mission: Provide food for the hungry whilst striving to end hunger in our city.

Our four core strategies are:

- *Increase quality and supply of food*

- *Strengthen existing distribution channels and explore new channels according to community need*

- *Expand programmes that address the root causes of hunger*

- *Enhance public education and advocacy on issues of hunger.*

Our target for this year: 250,000 kg of food distributed.

It was all so simple, thought Bill. Every shift that packed food, every food box filled and every can of beans packed in a box contributed to achieving the mission. If only it were that simple at Ascent!

People at the Food Bank worked quickly, and happily, demonstrating teamwork and enthusiasm. A few old hands could be a bit bossy, but people accepted each other's foibles and got on with the job at hand. At the end of the shift, the volunteers took brooms and brushes from a cupboard, cleaned up spilt food and threw out waste packaging. Then came one of Bill's favourite moments – 'the huddle' – when Dan gathered all he volunteers together to sum up.

"OK everyone," he began. "I'm sure you're interested in knowing what we achieved this morning." He looked down at the sheet of paper in his hand and announced, "Despite some trouble with the box sealing machine you packed 164 Family Food Boxes today. Give yourselves a round of applause – you deserve it! Very well done everyone."

People cheered, congratulated one another and generally looked pleased with themselves.

"Remember," said Dan, "We love to receive your donations of money or food, but what we really need is your time. Without it, none of this is possible. So tell your friends, your family, and your work colleagues that the Food Bank needs them. We've got to pack 250,000 kg of food this year. Because of you, needy people in the Westkirk area will have decent food to eat. Thank you!"

No wonder people keep coming back, thought Bill. How often do you get so much satisfaction from a morning's work?

At that moment the penny dropped for Bill. He grinned broadly as he got an inkling of how he might patch up his problems at work.

"Do you want that chat?" asked Dan as Bill walked past him.

"I think you have already solved my problem!" replied Bill, still grinning.

"I guess you worked it out for yourself," said Dan, "but since this is such an inspiring place, we'll accept some of the credit."

On his way out, Bill used his phone to snap a photo of the blue banner and set off for home contemplating Monday with a smile.

Team Meeting

Bill sat at the head of a long table surveying his team, who filled the meeting room. As usual, there was a plenty of good-natured banter as they settled down after the weekend and prepared to discuss the week's priorities in their regular Monday morning meeting.

Many of the team were in their early twenties and all but two were men. Several were not long out of university and still dressed like students. Only a few looked like they might work for an insurance company. Bill could see why a few senior managers referred to them as 'The Geek Squad'. They had more than enough IQ for the job at hand, but were not over-endowed with the emotional intelligence necessary to build good relationships with their customers and to navigate the politics that were part and parcel of working at Ascent.

A little more finesse and a little less brainwork would help raise the team's prestige and success, thought Bill. He knew he was just as guilty as any of them of focusing too much on technology and not enough on what their work meant for the business. But this was all about to change.

"Good morning, everyone. I trust you all had an excellent weekend," he began, glancing around the room with a smile, bringing everyone's attention to the meeting.

Once the usual discussions about project issues and priorities had been completed, Bill declared, "Today, I'm introducing a new agenda item – it's entitled 'Purpose'. As we're all well aware, Project Connective goes live next month..."

There were a few coughs and murmurs as people contemplated the arrival of a long-overdue system that had been beset by major technical problems and scope changes as people in the business changed their minds about what they wanted.

"Here's a simple question," said Bill looking slowly around the room before asking "What is the purpose of Connective?"

The question was met with nervous laughter from those most closely involved with the project. They had been looking forward to drawing a line under it and moving on to something less frustrating as quickly as possible. Questioning its purpose at this late stage was perplexing – and a little alarming.

Bill paused, waiting with interest to see what people would come up with.

Charlene Redstone, a junior Systems Designer involved with the project, sat forward in her chair, swept a few loose strands of dark hair behind her right ear and began tentatively,

"Well, it's a whole re-platforming and integration of the databases. The infrastructure is going to be stabilised and the risk of data corruption will be greatly reduced. The upgrade to a relational database means faster data access, real-time reporting and user-defined functionality enhancements. We are rolling a single, unified customer view to all end-users across the whole company." Charlene's voice trailed off as she searched round the room for a positive reaction to her words, and, when none was forthcoming, she took a sudden interest in the notes on the table in front of her and shuffled a few papers.

"Good, Charlene," said Bill, trying not to betray his disappointment that one of his best people could not describe the purpose of their most high-profile project in a way that would make any sense to their colleagues in the rest of the business. It was also a painful reminder of his own shortcomings in communicating their work. More than once, he had proudly presented stacks of slides crammed full of technical jargon and wondered at people's lack of enthusiasm for the systems that he and his team had worked so hard to deliver. But all of that was about to change.

"That's a good description of what we are doing," he continued. "It's a real breakthrough for us in creating a more flexible and easily-extendable IT infrastructure. It's a big thing for everyone in this room, and it's going to make our lives a lot easier, but it's not what's going to make life better for people in the business. Perhaps I should have asked, 'What does Connective mean to our customers – the people who work in Operations – and perhaps even what does it mean to their customers – the people we insure?'"

Bill's questions were met with a period of silence followed by a couple more long-winded attempts to pin down the project's purpose, which overflowed with jargon and hinted only vaguely at its true purpose.

Bill had anticipated this outcome and now moved on to the next phase of his plan. "As you all know," he said, "Connective has been a long time coming. It's been a real test of our skills, our determination and our patience. So it's really no surprise that the difficulties and frustrations we've experienced have distracted us from the one thing we are all here for; to make Ascent the most admired insurer in Europe." He paused and looked from one furrowed brow to the next as people struggled to make the link between the problematic Connective project and Ascent's vision: 'To become the most admired insurer in Europe'. Bill felt strongly that Connective's purpose must ultimately contribute to achieving the company's vision just as everything that happened at the Food Bank was connected to their mission. Otherwise, they had no business doing the project at all. He was convinced that to get the business fired up about Connective all they needed to do was to make the link clear and explicit.

"With that in mind," continued Bill, "I'd like everyone on the Connective team, even if you are not on it full-time, to re-visit your priorities for the week. I'd like you to work together on a new, high-priority goal – defining purpose of Connective. I suggest you speak to the people on the receiving end of Connective, i.e. our customers, to identify the essence of what they want from the new system – what's their vision? Once you know that, you should work on creating a single sentence that uses the plainest English you can muster to communicate a clear and compelling purpose. It's going to be tricky, but I know you have the brains and imagination to make it happen."

I appreciate how busy everyone is, but this is as important as anything on your priority list. Put simply, it's the difference between success and failure for Connective. Your heroic efforts deserve to be recognised by the business. That can only happen if we create a clear and compelling purpose. I'm here to help if you need me, but I trust you to get it done the way you see fit. Who's up for the challenge?"

"I think it's a great idea," said Justin O'Connor, one of the Project Managers assigned to Connective, "and long overdue. We were pretty revved up at the beginning of the project, but that was so long ago I can barely remember it, and I have to confess that I have lost sight of the target."

Soon there was general agreement that the task was an important one, and Justin and Charlene volunteered to co-ordinate the effort.

"So then, we're agreed," said Bill. "By next Monday, we will have a clear purpose for Connective, so we can then plan how to get the message out to our colleagues. Thank you all very much." With that, the meeting ended and a few of the team gathered around a whiteboard to map out how they were going to meet Bill's challenge.

One Week Later

One week later, there was an unmistakable air of excited expectation in the room just ahead of Bill's weekly team meeting. People chatted more loudly than usual and there was a lot of laughter. Charlene and Justin looked particularly pleased with themselves.

Bill knew his challenge had triggered a wave of activity during the previous week, but he had resisted the strong temptation to get involved, which was just as well as the team seemed determined to keep things secret until Monday.

"I get the feeling we'd better make Connective the first item on today's agenda, otherwise we won't get much attention for anything else. Is that right?" said Bill, looking at Charlene.

"Yes," replied Charlene keenly, "we're ready. Justin, do you want to kick off with an explanation of what happened?"

Justin was a tall, gangly 25 year-old Irishman with a long pale face and wispy goatee beard. "OK, yeah," he began hesitantly, his bright eyes flicking around the room, "Er...we thought it would be good to spend some time telling everyone what happened last week because it seems to us that the process we went through may have been as useful as what we got out of it."

"It's fair to say, asking people the purpose of Connective got some pretty interesting reactions." People in the room began to laugh. "I think they were a wee bit surprised that we were asking them about the purpose of our project. That was lesson number one. We had to adjust their thinking so they could see that it was, in fact, their project, and we were just there to help make it happen. That was a bit of a shock for some of us as well." Bill joined in the general laughter. Justin was beginning to warm to his own performance.

"Once they'd taken that on-board we got them thinking and talking about what they wanted. Of course, we had to keep them within the bounds of what the system could actually do for them rather than just coming up with a wish list. That was lesson two;

how to focus their thinking on the real benefits of the system. What worked well was asking them to project themselves into the future and imagine what it would be like when Connective was in place; what would it do for them and what would it do for their customers? That's when they started to generate solid ideas we could all work with. We began to see that it was all about transforming the experience our existing customers have when they call us. Now I'd like to hand over to Charlene for the next bit."

Charlene stood up. "Right, so we had a lot of ideas about how to describe the purpose of Connective. The next challenge then was to boil them down into something that was going to grab people's attention and galvanise them into action. So, a few of us got together with a couple of the users and bashed the ideas around for most of a morning before coming up with something that started to feel right. The big lesson for me was the value of having our customers in the room to give their perspective as, in the end, that's what counts. Also, we needed to make a big effort to stop thinking about the wizzy technical features of the new system and even to stop focusing on operational benefits like faster processing speeds or more user-friendly reports. We had to keep asking 'What is this fundamentally about?' A useful test was whether we could get excited about the purpose we had come up with. If not, it was back to the drawing board."

"So, after all that effort you'd better like what we came up with," she said, smiling and picking up a roll of brown paper. Justin stood next to her and between them they rolled out the paper like a banner for everyone to see. In foot-high letters it simply read: "One and done."

Bill smiled broadly. "Yes, that's great. In fact, it's brilliant!" he exclaimed. The more he thought about it the more he liked it. It was now a matter of putting it to work.

Four Months Later

Four months later, following another shift packing food (one of several that followed the cold Saturday morning that inspired him to find a purpose for Connective) Bill and Dan finally sat down for a cup of tea at the Food Bank. They chatted for a while before Bill told Dan what had happened.

"I realised that a big part of the magic here," said Bill, looking around him, "is a powerful sense of purpose. It's everywhere – on all those banners – and you keep repeating it to the volunteers. That's what was missing at work. We were too busy focusing on the baked beans, so to speak, to appreciate that we were feeding the hungry."

"It's no good putting the beans in the right spot if nobody knows why they're doing it," said Dan, taking another sip of tea from his mug.

"Exactly," agreed Bill. "We got into a situation where we were delivering change by the truckload without paying attention to why we were doing it. It was like producing bright, shiny new gadgets, but not advertising them. Then we wondered why our customers seemed so indifferent or even hostile to our products. They viewed what we did as a distraction from the real work of serving customers and growing the business. It seems so obvious now, but you can't expect people to put in a load of effort to change the way they work if they don't have a strong sense of why they're doing it. Now, I wonder why on earth it took us so long to figure it out – not like here at the Food Bank."

"Oh no, we have the same issue here every week," countered Dan. "People show up with a vague idea about doing something worthwhile. It would be easy to get them to work for a few hours and send them on their way. We even get school kids in here who have been told they will 'volunteer' and who arrive with the aim of doing as little as possible. My goal is to get volunteers to connect with our mission, so they return again and again – and even bring friends and family along. That's why I spell out our mission at the beginning and end of each session. Anyway, back to you and your mission. What did you come up with?"

"Well, first, I probably need to explain a bit about our new IT system, called Connective. I don't know what your experience has been of calling an insurance company or a bank, but most people find it pretty frustrating being passed from one person to another and being told, "Sorry, we only deal with home insurance. If you have a query on life insurance I'll need to put you through to someone else or get someone to call you back". Anyway, we had that problem in spades. We were split into so many different divisions, all with separate IT systems, that we ended up bouncing our customers all over the place. It was losing us business."

We knew what Connective did; it gathered information from different systems into one place. We set about asking why we wanted to do it. I know it might seem obvious, but we wanted to keep digging until we had a clear and compelling purpose that people could connect with, like they do at the Food Bank. We needed something strong enough to inspire change. Saying it would help break down barriers between the business divisions was a start. Saying it would improve the way we dealt with customers was even better, but we wanted something more, and, after a fair bit of work, we found it by coining the phrase "One and done" to describe a single operator resolving all customer issues in a single call."

"I like the sound of that," said Dan.

"Yes, so did I – and, more importantly, so do our internal customers. In fact, they were so taken with the idea that it's became their mission to achieve 100% 'One and done', which is a serious challenge that will take quite some time to achieve. It's already meant changing the way people work as individuals and teams and breaking down the barriers between divisions. Another great thing was that the business picked up the ball and ran with it. It was no longer just another IT project, but a business initiative. It was like releasing a pressure valve. There was a sudden flood of activity to prepare the way for the arrival of Connective. 'One and Done Teams' were created to work out how to exploit the system to maximum effect and to train phone operators to handle a wider range of issues. Some of the most experienced operators became 'One and Done Coaches' supporting people as they learned new skills. It's already a success, with over 82% of calls being resolved in one go by a single operator."

"As for my team, it's become a running joke that every time someone wants to start up a new project we ask, "Why is that important?" and we keep on asking, "why, why, why?" until we either have a convincing purpose that contributes to our mission or we send people back to the drawing board."

"And all of that came from packing food," said Dan with a broad smile.

"Yes," said Bill, "inspired by a can of beans!"

2. THE PROFESSOR

An Albert Ross Factory

"It's one thing to see what world-class looks like, but I'm buggered if I can get it to work here," said Cliff Bennett, Factory Manager at Albert Ross Engineering, to Libby Needham from the Central Performance Improvement Team.

"I've told the production line managers and the shift leaders exactly what to do. They've even agreed with me what's required, but if you go out there," said Cliff, pointing at the wall of his office in the general direction of the production lines, "you'll see damn all has changed. Even the tidying up blitz they did two months ago has gone to pot. It's as chaotic as ever out there!"

"Sounds like you need the Professor," said Libby calmly as she sat watching Cliff getting worked up by the lack of progress achieved in implementing 'Kaizen' continuous improvement practices in his factory. She had seen the same thing happening at other Albert Ross sites, and knew there was only one antidote – and a rather odd one at that.

"The Professor?" asked Cliff, puzzled.

"Yes, The Professor practically invented this stuff and he's been a great help at our other factories. Here's his contact details," said Libby, tearing a page from her notebook before standing up and handing it to Cliff. "Word of warning though, he can be, let's say, a little interesting to work with."

"I hope he can work miracles," said Cliff forlornly.

"Go to the gemba," said Libby, as she walked to the door.

"What?" said Cliff.

"Good luck," said Libby.

Cliff took a deep breath as he studied the piece of paper with the mobile phone number on it and was about to reach for his phone when he thought better of it and decided to email the Professor instead.

The Visit

Cliff did not receive a reply to his email. However, two days later, someone pressed the buzzer at the back door of the factory and Jim Carnaby, one of the production team leaders, opened it to let in a small, very neatly dressed man who looked to be in his fifties and to come from somewhere in the Far East.

"Can I help you?" asked Jim, eyeing the visitor and wondering if he had wandered into the factory by accident.

"I am here to see Mr. Cliff Treaves," said the visitor, bowing slightly.

Jim smiled and said, "Ah, you want the boss?"

"Yes please."

"Who do I say . . . ?"

"Professor Yamashina, thank you," said the Professor.

"Hang on, I'll just tell him," said Jim, wondering what his boss would make of their exotic visitor.

"A Professor Yamashinner, or something like that, to see you, boss," said Jim, sticking his head into Cliff's office and grinning broadly.

"He's here?" said Cliff, surprised.

"Large as life. Well, when I say large, more like small and Japanese-looking," quipped Jim.

"Send him in. No, on second thoughts, I'll come out and see him," said Cliff, who was keen to meet anyone who could fix his production problems.

The Professor bowed slightly to Cliff, who, somewhat disconcerted, nodded in reply.

"I am Professor Yamashina."

"I am Mr. Cliff Treaves," Cliff replied, rather more formally than normal. "Please, come into my office."

"Are the production lines in your office?" asked the Professor.

"Well no," said Cliff, slightly put out. He was beginning to understand Libby's warning about the Professor being 'interesting' to work with.

"We go to see the production lines?" said the Professor, peering towards the production area.

"Well ... OK, why not. It's a bit of a mess right now, but why not?" said Cliff, glad of an excuse to get away from his emails for a while.

Cliff took the Professor on a tour of the first production line, and began outlining his problems in a low voice, so the operators wouldn't hear him, but loudly enough to be heard over the din of machinery.

"I've been to the best practice site at Yarmouth," he said. "I've tried everything to get things moving here. I've told them exactly what to do, down to the very last detail. I gave them plans and task lists. I even drew pictures for them showing them exactly how to do things, and nothing. No change at all. We've got the same kit, the same quality of staff, similar inputs and outputs, but nothing seems to take hold here in Melstan the way it has in Yarmouth. Down there, the whole team is really up for it, while here they can't seem to be bothered."

"I just can't get control of the situation. Besides which, people are cynical about any change. There've been so many in the past that have come and gone – Quality Circles, Process Re-engineering... You name it, we've had it. I can hardly blame them for being sceptical. I can't even get a grip on how we're doing now, let alone get it to world-class. In Yarmouth, they filmed the production area and used that to work out how to improve things, but because the unions won't let me film here, we can't get a handle on where we're wasting time."

"You want control of the production lines?" asked the Professor, struggling to be heard above the noise of the machinery.

"Yes, I do," said Cliff keenly.

"You know, Mr. Treaves, to gain control you must first lose it."

"Pardon?" said Cliff, hoping he had misheard the Professor.

"To gain control you must first lose it," said the Professor, looking Cliff in the eye.

That's all I need, thought Cliff, Eastern blinking philosophy. With that, his mobile phone rang and he excused himself before heading off to a quiet corner of the factory to take the call.

As he spoke to his boss on the phone, Cliff noticed the Professor heading for Production Line 4, and Eric Walters, one of the most hard-bitten, cynical team leaders in the factory. He winced at the thought of the Professor being fed into the cutting machine.

The Professor stood alongside Eric, reached into his inside jacket pocket, produced something that looked like a postcard and handed it to Eric before saying a few words. Eric said something in return, and then stood for a while studying the card and nodding to himself. Cliff was relieved to see the encounter had passed off without immediate harm. The Professor headed back towards him with a knowing look on his face.

Before Cliff could ask about the odd encounter with Eric, the Professor said, "Cup of tea?" and nodded toward Cliff's office.

"Well, Professor," said Cliff, handing him a mug of tea, "what advice do you have?"

"No advice. A dinner menu is no good to a starving man," said the Professor, who was definitely beginning to irritate Cliff.

"But I need help," said Cliff.

"You can only help yourself," countered the Professor.

"OK, I'll buy it," said Cliff, "How do I help myself?"

"Good. Three actions: 1. Give up control. 2. Go where things happen. 3. Teamwork."

"OK," said Cliff, hesitantly, "Just explain that a little more."

The Professor stood up and wrote the actions on Cliff's whiteboard. He spoke as he did so, "One, give up control – to gain control, you must first let it go. Two, go where things happen – the production lines, here and Yarmouth. Three, teamwork, well; I suppose you know what teamwork means. Thank you for inviting me."

With that, the Professor bowed and left.

Cliff sat at his desk, with his head in his hands.

"How was that, boss?" said Jim Carnaby chirpily as he stuck his head into Cliff's office to learn the outcome of the strange visit and beaming brightly at the sight of Cliff's deepening despair.

"Perhaps you should spend more time out on the line sorting things out instead of worrying about what I'm doing!" yelled Cliff, who immediately regretted losing his temper.

"OK, boss," said Jim unmoved, "I'm onto it."

Cliff remained closeted in his office the rest of the day, dealing with emails and making telephone calls. He finally stepped out at 7pm.

Things were quieter. Only two of the six production lines were running a late shift. Line four was idle, and his recollection of the Professor's encounter with Eric drew him to the line. As he approached it, he sensed something unusual. By the time he arrived, he was rubbing the back of his head and trying to work out what on earth had happened. Line four was cleaner and neater than he had seen it for ages. All the waste packaging was gone from under the workstations, the trolleys that cluttered and cramped the line as makeshift storage areas, had mysteriously disappeared. The storage areas themselves were more orderly than he had ever seen them before, and brand new labels had appeared indicating what belonged where. Cliff rubbed his chin, laughing and then scratching his head as he alternated between joy and confusion.

He returned to his office and took another look at the whiteboard. The Professor's list seemed less of a torment and more of an intriguing riddle that he was eager to solve. He picked up his mobile phone and texted Libby: "Can you make it to my office first thing tomorrow? It's important. You were right about the Professor. Help!"

The Next Day

The next day, Cliff came in early to catch up with Eric before the morning shift started.

"I'm impressed," said Cliff to Eric, surveying Line Four.

"Mmmm . . ." mumbled Eric, nodding and smiling slightly. This was a very positive reaction by his usual taciturn standards.

"What did our visitor have to say to you yesterday?" asked Cliff feeling, for once, that he might be able to have a conversation with Eric amounting to more than just grunts.

"He said, 'I am Professor Yamashina. Can you make this?'" With that, Eric took a photograph from the breast pocket of his overalls and handed it to Cliff. Cliff recognised it immediately. It was one of the neat and shiny production lines at Yarmouth.

"And so you just did it?" said Cliff incredulously.

"He said he was a professor," mumbled Eric by way of an excuse. Cliff handed back the photograph and Eric turned away before any further conversation might be required of him. Cliff was stunned by the simplicity and effectiveness of the Professor's approach. He could barely get Eric to speak to him, let alone persuade him to overhaul his production line.

"What the heck do I do?" Cliff asked himself back in his office. He took a deep breath and studied the whiteboard once more. In his mind, he heard the Professor saying, "To gain control first you must lose it." He hoped Libby would turn up soon to help him work out what to do next.

Half an hour later, she was in Cliff's office.

"I could really use some help working out how to turn the Professor's advice into some practical action," said Cliff anxiously.

"So, you got on well with the Professor?" asked Libby, sounding slightly surprised.

"Not exactly," said Cliff, "but it appears he knows his stuff. He may just be a miracle worker and I could do with a miracle."

Cliff explained the events of the previous day and his conversation with Eric. "That sounds just like the Professor," said Libby. "You're not the first to doubt him."

"What does he mean by all of this?" asked Cliff, gesturing to the three points on the whiteboard.

"He's suggesting how you can get started. Give up control, go where the action is and teamwork," said Libby, as if it was self-evident.

"I am no wiser," complained Cliff.

"That's OK. The point is to do something, not to theorise. Let's get Eric in and give him control over improving Line Four. Frankly, he's already taken control for himself so we may as well give him some help."

"You've done a great job on Line Four," Cliff told Eric, who had just joined them in Cliff's office. "How would you like to go to Yarmouth and see what else the Professor did and maybe report back on what you find?"

Eric rubbed the back of his neck and thought for a moment before saying, "I suppose I could take a look. It couldn't do much harm, could it? I should take a couple of my team with me."

Two days later, Eric and two of his team set off for Yarmouth to find out how they had managed to become a world-class manufacturing site. Libby had provided digital cameras to record what they saw. They returned the following day full of excitement and energy and asked if they could present what they had learned to the rest of the staff.

Over the following days, Eric and his colleagues presented to different groups in the factory fitting sessions around production plans and shift patterns. They had a series of photos printed out in large format and pinned to the training room walls. They talked about what they had seen in Yarmouth with great energy and enthusiasm and invited people to use Post-it notes to stick comments alongside each photo if they had a good idea about how to make the improvements work at their factory. They explained the advantages of having a clear-out and straightening up the production line and storage areas. They also introduced the Japanese concept of 'Kaizen', or continuous improvement. They joked about Japanese words they had learnt like 'muda', meaning effort wasted through inefficiency, and 'poke yoke', meaning error-proofing a process to deliver zero defects. They also explained the importance of 'going to the gemba', the place where the work is actually happening, to observe and improve it.

There was still a good deal of scepticism amongst the staff and a number of them began explaining why Yarmouth's approaches wouldn't work at Melstan. However, seeing Eric enthused about anything to do with work, they began to wonder if there might be something in these improvement principles after all.

Each production line was issued with a digital camera that people used to take photos of their work environment, which they posted up on the factory walls so people could suggest improvements.

The Return of the Professor

Three months after his first visit, Cliff invited the Professor back to the Melstan factory.

"Welcome back, Professor!" said Jim Carnaby brightly as he opened the back door to allow the diminutive figure to step in.

"He's back," said Jim to Cliff, who was standing near Line Two talking to the production team leader. Cliff smiled broadly when he saw the Professor.

"Good to see you, Professor," he said as he shook his hand warmly.

"Mr. Treaves – you are at the gemba?" asked the Professor with a trace of a smile.

"Yes," said Cliff, reddening slightly as he remembered his doubts about the Professor and his advice.

"You are improving," said the Professor as he looked around him.

"Yes, let me show you." With that, Cliff led him to the back of the factory.

"We used to have a storage area here, but we realised it was full of stuff we hardly ever used and so we threw almost everything away. That created so much space we were able to give staff a training area on the shop floor to practice new ways of working. I had thought we were going to need a factory extension, but since the clear-out, we have room to spare."

The Professor looked pleased.

"Shall we go and see Eric?" offered Cliff, "He's worked miracles on Line Four."

"Ah, yes – Eric," said the Professor.

Line Four had become the epicentre of the factory's improvements. Many of the new ideas that people came up with were trialled by Eric and his team.

Eric gave the Professor a tour of the line. "So far, changes in the way work flows through the factory have improved efficiency by over 12%," he boasted. "That's on top of production line efficiencies, and we're now aiming to get our error rates below 0.5%."

"Zero," said the Professor, "zero is a beautiful number."

Eric rubbed the back of his neck. "Fair point, Professor...we're now aiming to get error rates to zero."

The Professor smiled at Eric who seemed uncharacteristically eager to please.

"You really saved our bacon," said Cliff, "we were at the bottom of the productivity league. Now, we're one of the top three sites, and I believe we'll soon be number one, thanks to Eric and others. I now know exactly where all the time and effort goes at every stage of every process. But the best bit is that the guys come to me now if they spot muda, usually with a suggestion on how to remove it. I've been at this job for over four years, and I thought it was time to move on, but now I enjoy coming to work every day. It's a real buzz," said Cliff, his eyes shining. "I know we've got a long way to go and a lot of work to do to come anywhere near world-class, but I'm actually looking forward to it."

"You're right," said the Professor. "You are at the start of a long journey, but I have high hopes for you. You have a highly competent and enthusiastic team."

"Thank you," said Cliff.

"You have control," added the Professor.

"Yes, but only after I gave it away!" said Cliff. At this, both laughed and shook hands enthusiastically before the Professor headed off with an open invitation to return any time he liked.

3. FRENZY

The Hall of Fame

"What strikes you about the 'Hall of Fame'?" asked George Kwela quizzically. Mike Gillon considered the photos and memorabilia lining the walls of the long corridor connecting their offices to the canteen know as Frenzy's 'Hall of Fame'. The display began with a photo dated 1978 showing Roy Halden and Jeff Marsh – former drummer and lead guitar of the Dambusters and founders of Frenzy – at the opening of the first Frenzy music store in London's trend-setting Campden Lock Market. Other photos showed them opening new stores, attending Live Aid in 1985, and handing out the 'Frenzy Awards' that recognised progressive music artists. A framed first edition of Frenzine, Frenzy's music magazine that was famous for its definitive music reviews and uncanny ability to spot new trends, hung in a place of honour.

"It's impressive stuff," said Mike, "you can really see why people love this company. It's always been about cool, cutting-edge music. What a great brand."

"Yes, it's fantastic. Otherwise, we wouldn't be here," said George, the new Chief Executive of Frenzy who was tasked with turning around the ailing music retailer. Mike was his Chief Financial Officer and trusted advisor in several similar campaigns in other businesses. "But what else strikes you about this place?" asked George.

Continuing down the corridor, Mike pondered George's question. George had halted in front of the final huge photo of a concert put on especially for hundreds of Frenzy's employees, plus their friends and families, to celebrate the new millennium. The people in the photo were cheering and dancing and looked like they were having the time of their lives.

Mike stood next to George, who, although shorter, was broader and immaculately dressed in a silver grey Italian suit and bright floral tie. He wore a large gold Rolex and his black shoes shone brightly. Mike was amused by how out of place he looked alongside the images of wild rock musicians.

"It all ends here!" exclaimed George looking from the photo to Mike and then back to the photo again. "There's nothing new since the first of January 2000. The history of Frenzy ends here. We're on board a ghost ship!"

Mike nodded in agreement. "Yes, I guess it does seem that way. I'm sure they know the world's moved on since then, but you can't really blame them for not celebrating it."

The beginning of Frenzy's decline in fortune could be traced back to the early years of the new millennium with the arrival of music downloads, both legal and illegal. At first, the dent in revenues had been a minor irritation. But as MP3 players caught on and revolutionised how people bought music, the irritation quickly turned into disaster. High street stores, even cool, trendy one like Frenzy, started to seem irrelevant. They were forced to close many of the stores before they were eventually taken over by a venture capital group who thought that Frenzy, with its strong brand and reputation, could become a major player on the internet.

"That's what I like about you, Mike," George said, still studying the final chapter in the Hall of Fame. "You rationalise everything – the perfect finance man. Me, I see this and I want to tear the whole thing down. It's like an invisible force holding everyone back!"

George and Lily

"It's ironic," George told his mother, Lily, "the music business is about new, new, new; one minute you're nobody, the next you're a star with thousands of people adoring you. Then, a year later, they adore someone else and you're nobody again. It's all change, change, change, but trying to change things at Frenzy is like pushing an enormous rock uphill. Just when you think you've got somewhere it rolls back to the bottom again." George was perched on the edge of the sofa in his mother's living room, while she sat in an armchair and studied her son, who seemed as animated and intense as ever. She liked that he still discussed his problems with her, but she knew from long experience that he was too headstrong to listen to much of her advice.

"You know you are asking a lot of these people," she began in her slow, gentle voice, "they love their company, and you're trying to turn it into something else."

"Well, they really have no option. This isn't about me and what I want; the world has moved on, and we'll become an irrelevant relic of history unless we do too! They say a captain should go down with his ship, but I say 'I'm from Botswana, where there's no coastline and no navy, and no interest in that tradition!'"

"Yes, I know full well where you are from and your attitude to tradition," frowned Lily. "Remember that you're the new boy. Maybe you should try seeing things from their point of view. Remember, you've had to deal with change all your life, from the moment you arrived in this country as a child. You love change. You thrive on it. But remember their tradition is in their bones."

"Well, a lot of good tradition did for Pa," countered George, his arms waving about as he warmed to the debate, "He stuck with the old ways and where did it get him? One leg in Botswana and one in England, and belonging nowhere." Lily's dark eyes dropped to her lap and George could see that he had upset her. His father had died just over a year ago, and George cursed himself for bringing him into the conversation so bluntly.

"I'm sorry Ma, but you know what I mean. I wasn't trying to upset you. You know, all of this stuff at work makes me wonder how you did it. Pa was stuck in his ways; traditional food, traditional music, always hanging out with people from the old country. But you were different. How did you manage to adopt England as your home, and to still not forget where you came from? What's your secret?"

"Well, it wasn't all that hard. I had you and your father for a start; his mind in one country and yours in another. You remember what you did when you were just seven years old?"

"Yes, Ma," said George wearily, knowing she was about to retell a story he had heard a hundred times before.

"You came home from school one day," Lily continued undeterred, "and you went to your bedroom, and you took everything that linked you to Botswana and put it all in a sack and threw it out of the back door. Your drum, your blanket, everything. From that instant you were an English boy and never looked back. You became 'Prince George' as your Pa called you."

George still squirmed at the mention of the nickname his father had used, half mockingly, half proudly, when George spoke in his very correct BBC accent and dressed 'like an English gentleman'.

"Yes," said George, "I know, but I'm asking about you."

"About me?" said Lily as if she was an unimportant subject. "Well, you know me; I make the best of things. I have an English china teapot and an African drum. I don't forget the past, but I do look to the future, whatever it may bring."

George smiled at his mother's easy optimism and looked at the small drum on the bookshelf beside her chair. It was the one he had tried to throw out aged seven. His mother had rescued it and kept it hidden until after his father had died.

"You can have it," Lily said, indicating the drum, "It's yours, after all."

"But it goes with your teapot."

"I have others. Your father made sure of that."

George wanted the drum and his mother knew it. He went over to the bookcase and picked it up. The musty smell of the animal skin and wood filled his nostrils and transported him to his childhood and to memories of his father. He turned away as tears welled up in his eyes and pretended to study the drum in the light from the window.

Wiping his eyes surreptitiously, he turned and sat down again.

As he looked around the room at his mother's collection of photos and other mementos of his father he was reminded of Frenzy's Hall of Fame and the difficulty he was having getting them to 'look to the future, whatever it may bring'. His eye settled on a photo of his younger brother's daughter, Emily, born six months earlier. He smiled at her cute round face and big eyes. He imagined what she might be like as an adult and the kind of world she would grow up in. What would she know of her grandpa and his longing for a distant land? Maybe one day she would visit their home village, if it was still standing. Her life is a new chapter in the family history.

"It's time I helped them put their past behind them!" exclaimed George, jumping to his feet.

"In a sack?" teased his mother as George leant down to kiss her cheek. "Don't be a stranger," she called out as he hurried out the front door.

Plotting a Revolution

George Kwela, Mike Gillon and Gayle Hart, Frenzy's HR Director, were preparing for a two-day executive workshop at the local conference centre.

"It's about mental attitude," said George, referring to his fellow board members. "Over the last couple of months, we've had great discussions about what it's going to take to turn us into a significant player on the web, to really get the Frenzy brand out there and make some waves in the industry. They've been full of exciting ideas and energy, but the very next day, they're back to fussing about artwork for store till displays. There's only ten stores left – and they're supposed to reflect what we're doing online, not the other way round. We've got to get them thinking like a dot com instead of a high street retailer."

"They've grown up with those stores," said Gayle. "Most of them started their working life behind the counter, and some probably wish they were still there chatting to customers about heavy metal, techno or suchlike. It's in their DNA."

"And if they could still sell it on vinyl so much the better," said George with a slight snort.

"Anyway," he continued, "I've got some ideas about how we can stir things up. It's time for revolution!" He grinned widely at the prospect and laughed at Mike, who looked pale as he contemplated the long weeks of hard work ahead of them turning George's latest dream into reality.

"Gayle, I need all of your creative flair on this one. It's time to write the next chapter!" said George, impatient to break through the barriers that had frustrated him for weeks.

The Executive Workshop

There were greetings all round as Frenzy's executives trailed into the conference room. George, Mike and Gayle watched their fellow directors peer at the single long sheet of white paper stuck to three of the walls. The paper was blank, except for a series of dates, beginning in one corner of the room at 1978 and reaching 2000 at the end of the second wall. Three large, brightly-coloured blue, red and yellow plastic crates stood at the front of the room. In the middle of the room were ten swivel chairs; one for each person attending the session.

"Are we going to have a history lesson?" asked Jill Fox, Marketing Director.

"More of a history quiz," replied Gayle, "nothing too taxing; just popular music with a twist."

"So George, are you the quiz master?" asked Phil Williams, the Operations Director. Phil had been with Frenzy from its inception. He dressed more like a biker than a retail executive, wore his hair in a long grey ponytail and was highly suspicious of the new owner's plans for Frenzy.

"No, you're the experts. I'm just along for the ride," replied George. Phil was very influential in the company, and George was keen to get him onside – although he feared he would be a tough nut to crack.

People settled into their chairs, looking slightly unsure of themselves with no boardroom table on which to place their numerous electronic devices and folders.

"Good morning," said George, "Today, as you know, is about planning the future of Frenzy. But we cannot plan the future without understanding the past, so we have a treat today. It's a music quiz. I hope you're up for a bit of fun to get the session going!"

A number of the board members glanced at each other looking a little reluctant to play games, especially one dreamt up by George.

"As you can see," began Gayle, "the quiz is about dates. The idea is to plot events in the history of popular music and events in the history of Frenzy on the walls around you, starting in 1978 and ending in 2000. In the coloured crates are images of these events. Your job is to work as a team to match the events to the correct dates. The blue crate contains music events, the red one contains Frenzy events and the yellow crate contains more general events. You have 30 minutes to complete the exercise, so please go to it."

With that, Gayle hit a button on a remote control and the unmistakable sound of a Jeff Marsh guitar solo drifted out of the speakers positioned in the front two corners of the room. As the opening of 'Peaches', the Dambusters' most famous track, built towards a crescendo Phil William's chest and shoulder began to rise.

"That's more like it," he said. "Let's get on with this!" And with that, the team set about their task enthusiastically. Out of the coloured crates came various pictures printed on cards, each half a metre high. Out of the blue crate came photos of the opening of the first Frenzy store in 1978, the visit to the Brixton store by Sid Vicious of the Sex Pistols, and Roy and Jeff handing out the indie band prize at the Jupiter Music Awards. Out of the red crate came a poster of Blondie's 'Parallel Lines' tour dates with the year blacked out, the first album by The Clash and a headline announcing the death of John Lennon. Out of the yellow crate came images of the Bristol Riots, the first Star Wars movie and the release from prison of Nelson Mandela.

The team argued good-naturedly about the dates of events as the speakers filled the room with sounds of the 70's, 80's, and 90's. George joined in from time to time, but knew he could not compete with his team's encyclopaedic knowledge of music.

Within twenty minutes, the room had been turned into a collage of music culture spanning three decades and the board members were surveying their work with obvious pride.

"What do you notice?" asked Gayle.

"They don't write songs like they used to!" said Phil Williams. "Oh yes, and whatever happened to Frenzine? It was just so cool. We need it back."

"We've come a long way," said Vikki Lin, Retail Director, "It's amazing to see how much change we've been through. I remember when CDs came in and it was the death of vinyl. We all thought it was the end of the world and, before we knew it, it just seemed normal and we were wondering what all the fuss was about. And now, we're facing a monumental change, but I guess if we've survived all that, we can survive this." There were a few nods of agreement as people contemplated what Vikki had said.

Meanwhile, Gayle brought out a fourth, green-coloured crate from under a table at the back of the room.

"You've still got a bit more work to do," she said.

The directors began pulling out more images of events from the green crate, including images of an iPod, of Facebook, and of newspaper headlines proclaiming "Frenzy to Close 50 stores" and "Frenzy Sold to IB Capital". There was even a picture of George. The mood became more sombre as the team plotted out the less glorious days of the new millennium.

At the bottom of the green crate was a large question mark.

"That's the future, I guess," said Vikki brightly.

"Hey, Gayle, have you got a purple crate hidden somewhere with pictures of the future?" asked Phil.

"As you know," said Gayle, "that's what we're going to do today and tomorrow. We're going to create the future."

"But before we do that," said George, "as I am still the new boy around here I'd really appreciate it if you took me through all the important moments in Frenzy's history."

For the next hour, the team took George on a tour through the highlights of Frenzy's history. They recounted tales of the early years when people would visit the stores in the hope of meeting Roy and Jeff. There was the story of how Frenzine was sued after accusing a band of lip-synching to their songs on TV, only to be vindicated. They also recalled people queuing around the block for new albums by the likes of Joy Division or U2, and they spoke about the midnight vigils held outside several stores the day John Lennon was shot. Finally, the discussion turned to more recent events and the difficult years that had brought them to this point.

"We were devastated when we had to shut so many stores and lay people off who'd been with us for years," said Vikki. "There were a lot of tears. Then we were sold and Roy and Jeff went, and it seemed like the heart went out of the place. A lot of people have been sleepwalking for some time. You know, we've been getting on with things, but not really engaging our hearts and souls like in the old days. We used to lead the industry and now we're followers."

"We're not even followers, we've been left behind," added Phil.

"What makes me angry," continued Vikki "is the waste. Look at all of this. Look at everything we've achieved. We've touched thousands of lives and made them better. Now it's all heading for the scrap heap." Others joined in to explain how bad they felt about letting down so many of their former employees and how the sight of Frenzy being sold 'like a can of beans' broke their hearts.

Eventually, everyone sat down and contemplated the situation in uneasy silence before George asked, "So, what next?"

"It seems to me we have a choice," said Phil, looking around the room. "We can consign this lot to history or we can create the next instalment. We can take what's best from our past and make it work in the future. We've got millions of loyal customers out there who are desperate to see us get back on track."

"So, how do we make Frenzy great again?" asked Gayle.

"You know what," said Vikki, "we really haven't been open as a group about just how badly we're doing, until today that is. We need to stop living as if the glory days of Frenzy are still here. We need to admit the failures, and then put them behind us and move on."

"Yes, I agree with Vikki," said Phil, "We may never recapture the glory days, but we've got to move forward. Whatever happens, it's got to be better than sinking slowly into the mire."

George Looks Back

"The turning point came two years ago when the board of Frenzy decided to re-invent the company," said George to the TV interviewer as he leaned back looking relaxed on the 'Business Breakfast' sofa. He glanced up for a moment recalling that first day at the conference centre when some genuine enthusiasm for change had been ignited amongst his fellow directors. They had worked late into the evening and then continued talking excitedly into the night, downing several drinks in memory of 'Old Frenzy' and in celebration of the birth of 'New Frenzy'. There had been much recollection of the 'good old days' and excitement about recapturing the magic of Frenzy in the twenty first century.

By the next day, they were like a bunch of school kids let loose for the summer holidays. Ideas flew, and New Frenzy took shape, including plans to mobilise the whole workforce around the vision to 'Make Frenzy great again'.

"We had so many fans out there," continued George, "people who loved what we stood for in the world of music and wanted us to succeed, but we were struggling to let go of the past. The secret was to hang on to the core of what had made us great and shed things that were holding us back. As my mother always says, 'Never forget the past, but always look to the future, whatever it may bring'. But that's easier said than done – letting go of things you hold dear and are so much a part of your identity. They can become a trap imprisoning you in your past."

"And now you're riding high as one of the fastest growing online businesses in the world," said the interviewer enthusiastically.

"We were very sad to lose our high street stores. We lost the day-to-day, face-to-face contact with people. On the other hand, now we touch millions of people all over the world, people who share our passion for music.

"Bringing back Frenzine and putting it on the web was a master-stroke," enthused the interviewer.

"Yes, it was," agreed George. "It really put us back in touch with our core market – people who love innovation and who are always on the lookout for great new bands and new music. We've found ourselves leading the way again, rather than following the crowd. There was an explosion of creativity in the company once people realised how powerful and immediate our impact could be. Now, every aspiring band and singer is queuing up to have their videos released on our site. It's such an exciting place to be!"

"So why are you planning to step down as CEO?" asked the interviewer pointedly.

George smiled and gave a gentle laugh. "My job is over. I was just the guy that helped people free themselves from their past. The business really belongs to the people who have grown up with it, people with music in their blood."

The New Hall of Fame

Meanwhile, at Frenzy's offices the Hall of Fame had some new exhibits. Amongst them was a photo taken at the party celebrating the end of the 'Old Frenzy' and the birth of 'New Frenzy', a large flat screen TV switching between the most popular music videos on www.Frenzy.com, and a newspaper headline exclaiming 'Internet Frenzy!' One item stood out from amongst the rest; a small African drum stood at the transition point from the first incarnation of Frenzy to the second.

4. PERCENTAGE TENNIS

Tennis Buddies

Manish and Ravi were unlikely friends. They even looked mismatched. Manish was tall, strongly built, with a wide nose and heavy jaw, and he walked with an air of confidence. In contrast, Ravi was slight and wiry with twinkling eyes, sharp features and ears that stuck out. Their characters were equally different; Manish was loud, outgoing, competitive, and tough-minded, whereas Ravi was softly spoken and altogether more easy-going. Despite these differences, they had been firm friends from the time they had first met at school and now, when the weather was good, they played tennis together in the local park. They were well matched. What Ravi lacked in strength and height he made up for in agility and guile.

The two friends were also matched at work. Each of them ran a sales team for Regal Star, a beer company based in the town where they had grown up. Both had worked their way up from junior sales assistant. Manish had a reputation for being a demanding manager who was at his happiest personally intervening to rescue crisis situations. Alf Floyd, Manish's boss, liked his energy and drive, his no-nonsense approach and his focus on meeting sales targets. Alf was less sure of the diminutive Ravi, who seemed too laid back for the rough and tumble of the drinks trade, always wandering around chatting to his team, fussing about training and not driving hard to meet targets. As for Manish and Ravi, their friendship rose above any differences.

"You know, Ravi," said Manish to his old friend at the end of a tennis game as they sat on a bench drinking from their water bottles and mopping sweat from their faces and necks, "Now don't get me wrong, I enjoy our games of tennis, but, let's face it, we're not very good and we don't get any better from one year to the next. What I was thinking was, I saw this special offer in the local paper yesterday for half-price tennis lessons, and I thought we could sign up and give it a try. If we both did it then no one would have an unfair advantage. What do you say?"

Ravi thought about the proposal for a moment. He couldn't see much point in taking lessons, but knew his friend well enough to sense that he had already fixed in his head that he would take the lessons, so he agreed to go along with him. Anyway, he reasoned, it might be fun to learn how to play properly after all these years.

Regal Star

At work, there was pressure for improvement in the sales figures. The market for traditional beers and lagers was in steady decline. New competition had arrived several years earlier in the form of ready-mixed drinks – wines or spirits mixed with fruit juice and other flavourings. Younger people were increasingly opting for these so-called 'alcopops', which were marketed as cool, new-generation drinks – in sharp contrast to beer, which was associated with older people drinking in traditional pubs.

In response to market pressures, the new watch-word at Regal Star was 'diversification', which, in practice, meant selling beer through outlets other than pubs and bars. It meant approaching new customers like restaurants and cafes, and this meant change. Over the years, sales teams had formed strong working relationships with pub landlords and bar managers who gave them a steady stream of business. Approaching restaurants and other potential new customers offering Regal Star's range of wines, as well as its beers was a daunting prospect for many of them.

To prepare for the changes, a number of sales meetings had been dedicated to discussing the best ways to approach new customers. Sales scripts were written, target customers were identified and sales meetings set up. They had even conducted role-playing exercises to prepare themselves for a variety of situations they might encounter selling to new customers.

However, after three months of pushing diversified sales, the results were not good. In fact, things were going backwards, explaining why Alf Floyd was not looking happy as the sales managers gathered for their Monday morning meeting. He eyed up his team as they sat around the large meeting table studying the previous week's sales figures and the month-on-month sales figures for the year. It was clear the decline in sales was continuing unabated, especially over the past three months.

Alf broke the uneasy silence that had descended on the room by asking, "What's happening out there? This is the eighth week in a row of poor results. I'm getting major grief from Maggie." Margaret Hubble was the National Sales Director. "We have to turn this around or we'll all be looking for new jobs!"

The threat of job losses did not perturb the sales managers, who had heard the same warning for more than a year and it had now lost its impact. Nevertheless, they did not want to get on the wrong side of Alf as he could make life difficult and they knew well enough that the company, whilst still profitable, was under pressure from shareholders to cut costs. All training courses had been cancelled and travel costs were being squeezed. A lot was riding on diversification and Margaret Hubble would not hesitate to sacrifice people if scapegoats were required.

Silence fell once again.

"Ravi," said Alf, "your numbers are poor. You need to shove a rocket up people's backsides. If not, we'll be spending the rest of this year running twice as hard to catch up."

"We're in a bind. The guys are working really hard, but they're struggling to make inroads with new customers. They're not used to it..." Ravi trailed off as Alf fixed him with a look of impatience.

"The training period is over!" said Alf slapping his hand on the table and looking around the room to make sure every sales manager got the message. "It's time we stopped playing around and made things happen. Stop struggling and start selling!"

The sales managers could see the writing on the wall. Maggie had had one of her sessions with Alf, and he looked like a man who'd had the fear of G-d put into him.

As the meeting broke up, Alf took Manish to one side and said, "I was hoping for better from you. We need some leadership here. Show the rest of them the way." He gave Manish a friendly pat on the back.

"I'll make things happen," promised Manish.

Back on Court

Back on the tennis court, things were also not going to plan. Ravi and Manish had enjoyed their first lesson. The tennis coach had taken a look at their techniques and made a few changes, particularly the way they gripped their racquets. As a result, they were suddenly able to put in serves that were faster than anything they had managed before and the ball seemed to swerve and dip over the net as they learned how to apply slice to it. The two friends left the first lesson feeling like they had gained entry into a new world.

But their joy turned to pain a few days later when they tried out their newly acquired skills. It was like they had never played before. They struggled to get the ball over the net and when they did, it was apt to fly clean over the wire fencing surrounding the courts. Ravi watched as a furious Manish beat the ground with his tennis racquet as he attempted to locate another wayward shot that had sailed over the fence into a wild patch of undergrowth.

After less than an hour of this torment, they decided to call it a day. Ravi tried to calm his friend by saying, "It's just one of those things. We've got to take two steps back before we can take three steps forward. We'll get there in the end."

He could see that Manish's pride had taken a knock and his

impatience for success would not let him rest easy until he was playing to a standard that he could accept.

Things weren't much better the next time. Occasionally, they seemed to have things under control and pulled off a few excellent serves and dipping forehand shots. But these signs of hope were occasional glimmers amongst a carnival of netted shots and lost balls. Manish's face was dark with discontent.

Then, in the second set, Manish seemed to get a grip on things. He outplayed Ravi in every game until they once again sat exhausted on the wooden bench alongside the courts. "Nice play," said Ravi to his friend, "it seems to have clicked for you."

"Well, I have always been the better player," replied Manish with a laugh and giving Ravi a friendly punch on the shoulder.

"Of course," said Ravi, returning the punch, following a ritual they had enacted since their early days waiting for the school bus "I bow to thee, O supreme tennis champion." He followed this with an elaborate bow.

Back at Work

Manish was also turning things round at work. "Great results from Manish's team! Good work, Manish," said Alf appreciatively. Better sales figures from a few of the teams, especially Manish's, had improved his conversations with Maggie.

Alf surveyed the rest of his team leaders before leaning forward and speaking slowly, so no one could mistake the seriousness of what he had to say. "I now need to see improvement from every one of your teams. I hope I make myself absolutely clear." He eyed Ravi and wondered, not for the first time, if he was really suited as a team leader in such a tough business.

A week later, several teams had recovered and were once again hitting target. Ravi was now amongst the minority of team leaders failing to recover. In fact, he had fallen further behind. Alf took Ravi aside at the end of the Monday meeting and asked him why he was now the odd one out.

"It's just teething problems. I've been out with each and every one of my guys showing them what to do, coaching them through the sales meetings. They're finding it tough to adjust, but we'll get it right. I've told them to keep trying."

"Trying isn't good enough," said Alf, "results are what we need."

The following week, Ravi was edging back towards his target. A week later, a strange thing happened; Ravi's team went to the top of the sales performance league.

"How do you explain these figures?" Alf asked Ravi suspiciously.

"Well, we've finally cracked it, I guess," replied Ravi innocently, "it's just taken us longer than the others. It seems to be a slow and repetitive process getting to know prospective customers and building trust to the point where they eventually buy from us."

Alf wondered how he was going to backtrack on the suggestion he'd made to Maggie that Ravi be fired. Maybe it was just a blip in the figures and, in any case, Ravi had certainly not made up for his series of poor weeks.

But when Ravi's team remained top for the next two weeks, easily outstripping Manish and others, Alf began worrying that he would come under pressure to get the other teams up to the new standard set by Ravi's team.

Alf took Ravi aside at the end of the weekly sales meeting again. "How do you explain it? For weeks you got nowhere, now you're setting sales records." Ravi, who'd hoped for a friendly pat on the back, hid his disappointment.

"I guess it's like riding a bike for the first time. We scratched our knees, but got back on again," explained Ravi.

"But what about the other teams?" asked Alf, as if accusing Ravi of undermining their performance.

"I'll have a word if you like. Perhaps there's something they can learn from us," offered Ravi.

"That would be good. Yes, why don't you do that," said Alf, grasping at the only solution on offer to this new and perplexing problem of over-achievement.

The Coach

"How's it been?" asked the tennis coach, Rick. "Painful?"

"Yes," said Ravi.

"Usually is after the first lesson. No pain, no gain."

"Manish seems to have got the hang of it," said Ravi, looking across at his friend.

"Well, I wouldn't say that," said Manish awkwardly.

"Let's see what you've learned," said Rick.

Ravi was up first. He stood behind the service line and began serving, crashing the ball repeatedly into the net. Rick gave him a few words of advice about positioning his body and eventually, in amongst the poor serves, he hit a couple of beauties.

"Well done Ravi – great work," said Rick who was always full of positive encouragement. "Now your turn, Manish."

Manish stood behind the service line and hit some good steady serves over the net.

"OK, that doesn't look right, Manish. Let's look at that grip," said Rick before adjusting Manish's grip on the racquet to the new position, "Now try again."

Manish then followed Ravi's lead by crashing the ball into the net several times, while Rick helped him adjust his body movements slightly.

"Great, Manish," said Rick, "have another go. You're nearly there!"

With that, Manish hit a couple of beautiful serves before standing, hands on hips, admiring his own brilliance.

"That's outstanding," he said, "but how do I do that every time?"

"If you did that every time we'd be putting you in for Wimbledon," replied Rick. "Listen, the only way you can do this is to hit a lot into the net. It's about percentages; less than 20% failure on a serve like that and you play at Wimbledon; less than 40% and you wipe the floor with your friends. Failure is a big part of winning."

"What's your failure rate?"

"30 to 35%," answered Rick.

"Wow, that's great," said Manish.

"Yes, but I've hit tens of thousands of stinkers to get where I am," said Rick.

"Now, why don't you two play? But no going back to your old habits. Push those percentages," challenged Rick.

They played four games while Rick coached from the side-lines. Eventually, Ravi came out on top, though Manish came back strongly towards the end.

"Really well played, both of you," said Rick. "You stuck with it and you're making great progress. Make sure you practice a couple of times before we meet again. Remember, push up those percentages."

Back on the Bench

"All hail to thee, O supreme tennis champion", said Manish, bowing to his old friend after Rick had left.

"Rick's great," said Ravi. "It's not about winning or losing. He's only interested in getting us to improve."

"Sure," said Manish. "I still hate losing, but at least I'm learning, and winning will follow. No pain, no gain."

"It's a bit like work," said Ravi. The two friends sat for a while in silence, drinking from their water bottles and contemplating the sales league table, a subject which had been hanging unspoken between them for some time. Ravi thought he knew what Manish needed to do, but he wanted to wait for him to ask for help.

"You know what's happened?" asked Manish.

"I could maybe guess," said his friend.

"I went out with the guys this week. All they're doing is pounding the same old beat, trying to squeeze more sales out of the pubs and bars, but you can't get blood out of a stone. They're not even trying to get into the restaurants."

"Do you know why?" asked Ravi.

"Well, they found it tough chasing after new business. They weren't getting anywhere," said Manish pausing.

"And then what?" prompted Ravi.

"Then, I gave them a bollocking for not even making the old sales figures and they gave up altogether. They got back on track with the old targets, but they've no chance of making any big hikes without getting some new customers. What can I do?"

"No pain, no gain," said Ravi gently.

"I know", admitted Manish gloomily. "I need to tell them to forget about the targets for a bit and drive for new business. Seeing Rick today brought it home. I need to explain that it's about pushing up the percentages and taking some pain until the results start coming in. I need to pat them on the back for having a go even when they fail."

"OK, coach," said Ravi.

"Thanks, pal," said Manish. "Alf's going to give me a right ear-bashing over the next few weeks."

"Don't worry about Alf. I can square it with him now that I'm the new golden boy," said Ravi, punching his friend in the arm and getting one in return.

"All hail to thee, O supreme sales champion," said Manish, bowing low to his old friend.

Mrs Bromere 19. ? Slwte House
Mrs Barnes 44
Vernon 23
Norman Black 42 ✓
Harry Goldman 15

5. CRAZY TIME

Bad Day at the Office

Katie Brice slept fitfully, her head full of thoughts from the day before. Impending changes at work played on her mind through the night. The talk was of restructuring, changing job roles, new reporting lines and possible office mergers.

She got up early, determined to get a head start on what was likely to prove a difficult day.

Standing outside her office building, she was struck by how drab and dated it looked. The imposing block of red brick had been turned a dirty brown by decades of rain and traffic fumes; an image at odds with the government's vision of modern, efficient public services. Even Katie, who presided over this particular Community Housing office, could see how tempting it would be to shut it down. At the same time, the mere thought of merging with another office gave her a sharp pain in the pit of her stomach.

As she got closer, something seemed to be amiss. She headed quickly through the front door to find the offices in darkness. She noticed through the gloom that the clock above the front desk was stopped at ten past four and guessed there had been a power failure in the night. It was also freezing cold, so the heating must have shut down as well.

"Hayley!" she called out, in the hope the receptionist might be around to help her get the power back on. "Where on earth are you, Hayley?"

"She's not here today," said an unfamiliar voice from a dark corner of the lobby. There was a loud click and neon lights began to slowly flicker and splutter into life along the ceiling, revealing a bald, round-faced man in his sixties, dressed head to toe in black and standing atop a high ladder. "That's fixed it," he said with a wide grin. Katie had not seen him before, and wondered where the ladder had come from, but was glad he had found the fuse box and restored the power.

"Thank you," she said, relieved.

"Fuse blew. Must have been a power surge last night. All that lightening and whatnot," he said cheerily, descending from the ladder. "I'm Hayley's father. She's sick today and asked me to open up the office so nobody would be hanging about in the rain."

Katie's gratitude was tempered by surprise and irritation at Hayley's behaviour. Handing over the keys of a housing office to a non-employee, even to your own father, was a clear breach of security rules. She could not understand it. Hayley was normally so reliable.

Katie's phone began to rumble and ping. She searched her capacious handbag and eventually pulled it free. It rumbled again as she held it. Emails were rolling in thick and fast. She lifted her wrist to check the time, only to realise that in her hurry to leave home she had left her watch behind. She sighed heavily and scanned her emails quickly for anything that might shed light on the rumoured changes. She clicked on one from her boss entitled 'Update on Regional Strategy' and held her breath as she read it.

"Further to my previous strategy email," it began.

"What previous strategy email?" muttered Katie.

"As you will be aware, we are continuing to evaluate strategic options for the modernisation of Community Housing. Over the past months, a range of possibilities have been assessed," continued the email. "The results of this analysis process will be announced in the summer."

"The summer, when's the summer?" thought Katie, her anxiety rapidly turning into frustration.

The email went from bad to worse. "In light of the fact that the results of the analysis may lead to changes in people's roles, responsibilities and teams, Personal Development Reviews with your staff (which, I remind you, must be completed by the end of this month) should omit any definition of future personal objectives or personal training and development plans until the way forward is announced. The focus of reviews should be solely on past performance. Future plans should be left blank and only agreed once the restructure has been announced."

"What the hell are they up to?!" shouted Katie at her phone. "Have they gone completely mad? Have they any idea of the consequences of what they are asking? My entire team are already jittery about the review. The moment they're told not to plan their future objectives, they'll have their CVs on the market. There'll be utter pandemonium. And why use the word 'restructure'? A word like that will really set the cat amongst the pigeons. What on earth am I supposed to tell people when they ask me what's going on? I'm fed up with telling them that it'll all work out fine and jobs are secure when I have no idea what's going on. The summer is months away. The region is run by idiots!"

But the email had not finished yet. It continued, "We have employed a company called HadronPlus to work with us to shape our brand image. They will be contacting you this week to arrange to speak to you and your team as part of the process of defining our 'Who are we, and why are we here?' cultural statement."

"I'll give them a 'cultural statement' they won't forget!" thought Katie, starting to shake with anger.

Her phone rang. It was Hayley.

"Hello, I'm feeling a little bit sick today," said Hayley loudly. Her speech was slurred and there was loud music in the background and a hubbub of voices.

"Are you in the pub?" asked Katie astonished.

"Yes," said Hayley, "I thought a few vodkas would help with my sore throat." Hayley began to giggle uncontrollably.

"What the hell were you doing sending your father in to unlock the office!?" shouted Katie, beginning to think she was going mad.

"Who cares?" said Hayley still giggling. "We're all going to lose our jobs in the restructure anyway. HadronPlus are coming in tomorrow to fire us all. Why don't you come down here for a few vodkas to drown your sorrows? You sound like you need a drink."

Katie's phone began ringing loudly again, even though she could still hear Hayley giggling down the line. It was her boss. "Hi, Katie," said her boss. "Why aren't you taking the day off? We're heading out of town on a picnic if you want to join us."

"A picnic in the pouring rain!" said Katie. "You've got to be kidding. I'd sooner get things sorted out here."

There was a loud ping as a text arrived marked 'Urgent – immediate attention' from 'HadronPlus Outplacements'. It read 'Due to the planned regional re-alignment, you are now employed by HadronPlus under contract until your employment is terminated. You will cease operation now and report to our redeployment team next week and await further instructions. Thank you, HadronPlus – we care about outplacement." Katie let out a cry and hurled her phone at a wall on which had appeared an image of a fierce-looking black cat.

She woke up with a jolt and scrambled around on the bedroom floor looking for her alarm clock, which was ringing incessantly somewhere in the darkness.

"That's it," said Katie as she lay on the carpet clutching the now silent alarm clock. "It's time for a career change."

A Tale of Two Leaders

The period leading up to Katie's tussle with her alarm clock had been one of huge uncertainty. First there had been the final months of Eric Styles' reign as Regional Operations Director, or ROD. He was in charge of all of the branch offices, making him Katie's direct boss. Katie liked Eric; he asked for people's opinions, spoke openly and was not afraid to admit to mistakes. He met with Katie and the other branch managers regularly to discuss issues affecting the region and he was always keen to help out if they had problems. But she could not help thinking that he was a great branch manager who had been over-promoted.

Eric's biggest weakness was indecision. He spent forever canvassing opinions and chewing over issues, but was reluctant to make decisions and take action. Katie knew he lacked a cutting edge, and she was not alone in thinking the region had simply drifted along under his leadership. But it was only when outside events led to a crisis situation that his leadership was put to the test and found wanting.

There had been a prolonged rise in the property market, followed by a sudden crash. The property team had overspent during the boom time, so when the crash happened, they were faced with the double problem of a budget overspend and a rapidly rising demand for housing as people defaulted on their mortgages. Eric had been forced to slash the property maintenance budget and halt the purchase of new properties.

Staff in the region came under severe pressure from newly homeless people and those demanding repairs to existing homes. Two branch managers went off on long-term sick leave with stress.

People looked to Eric for decisive action, but little was forthcoming. One day he would tell people that it was vital to ensure that existing properties were kept in a good state of repair; the next he sent out emails about economising. A few days later, he was telling people they needed to give priority to a reduction in the waiting times for new housing. It became clear that he was simply reacting to events rather than taking command of the situation. No one could blame him for the property crisis, but the universal cry was "Just make up your mind!"

The situation came to a head when a local newspaper ran an expose on unsanitary living conditions in Community Housing and published photos of mould growing on damp walls, broken toilets and floors with gaping holes in them. Eric was called into the Regional Head Office and persuaded to take early retirement.

A new ROD, Ray Briggs, was quickly brought in from another region to replace Eric and charged with getting things back on track. Katie could not imagine anyone more different from Eric. Ray was a lean and shaven-headed forty-five year old who could not stay still for a moment, and talked rapidly about 'practical solutions', 'laser-beam focus' and 'making things happen'. He exuded energy – a supreme operations man who loved nothing better than fixing problems and driving action.

Ray had little time for contemplation, believing instead that determination and hard work were what counted. His many years of experience had cemented a fixed view about how things should be run, and whilst he asked a lot of questions, he did not give much away himself. This approach served him well at the beginning. Within weeks, maintenance work was focused where it should be, and a plan was emerging for reversing the overspend over the coming three years. Many of Katie's colleagues grumbled about Ray's aggressive style and limited listening skills, but they were impressed by his single-mindedness following the years of dithering that had marked Eric's tenure.

Katie too was a grudging fan in the early weeks. It was refreshing to see Ray dealing with problems that had undermined people's confidence in the leadership team and their pride in their jobs. But, like Eric, Ray had a fatal flaw, which only became clear several weeks after he arrived. It was then that people began referring to Regional Head Office as 'The Kremlin'. Information was sucked in from all quarters – constant requests were made to branch offices for budget information, operational performance data and improvement plans, but only a trickle of information came back the other way. What little did come out was full of 'management speak' and difficult to decipher. People spent a lot of their time poring over emails, trying to second guess what Ray was thinking and what he had in store for them in the way Kremlinologists had tried to decipher the murky communication that emanated from Russia during the Soviet Era.

When Ray did communicate, his preference was for 'set piece' presentations involving large numbers of people and just a few slides with little detail on them, which Katie suspected enabled him to avoid one-to-one interrogations in which he might feel obliged to explain himself or enter into the messy business of dealing with other people's opinions.

Word was out that Ray was assessing the whole region looking for opportunities to improve services and efficiency. Little information came directly from Ray or from the small, close-knit team of people he had gathered around him. This only served to intensify speculation about what he had in store for people.

Those with a pessimistic streak – and there were enough of them – talked of job cuts and redundancy, despite union agreement that jobs were secure. Even the optimists, who felt that things needed to change, were frustrated by the lack of clear direction about what they should do to improve performance. The suspense was slowly wearing everyone down and distracting them from their day jobs. New initiatives ground to a halt, since no one was prepared to invest time in them in case everything suddenly changed.

Katie 'bumped heads' with Ray on a number of occasions – asking him in group meetings for details, for a plan, for the who, what, when, where and especially the why of everything he was doing. Ray took this as a challenge to his authority and decided Katie was a trouble-maker who needed to be kept a safe distance away from the decision-making.

Then came the day of the 'big reveal' when Ray set out his plans for the region's future. No one was expecting it, so when the branch office managers wandered into another 'Update Meeting', they were relaxed and chatty, expecting another bland presentation devoid of detail. Instead, they got a new structure chart for the region, new job roles for themselves and a number of their staff, and new reporting lines, all in a matter of a few minutes.

A dispassionate analysis of Ray's proposals would have revealed that they made sense and would, with a few important adjustments, improve the way the region operated. But dispassionate views were thin on the ground that morning. People became very agitated and vociferously opinionated about even the smallest changes. The outcome of the meeting was a protracted and confrontational interrogation of Ray by a group of branch managers who had finally had enough of his apparent lack of interest in their views.

Ray seemed surprised by people's reactions, and said a number of times that his plans were 'based on the information you yourselves have given me.' He looked nervous and began to back-track on some of his proposals. This only encouraged people to become more militant in their views as they unloaded the frustration that had been building up over months of secrecy and impenetrable communication. In the end, Ray cut the meeting short, but not before explaining that change was inevitable, and his plans would be implemented.

It was that night Katie had her odd encounter with Hayley's father in her sleep. Two weeks later, she found herself outside the Regional Chief Executive's office feeling very nervous, but prepared to announce her plan to quit her job and, at the same time, wondering if she was about to make a big mistake.

Her attention was diverted by Ray Briggs, who was at that precise moment meeting with the chief executive, Ashley Cook. Katie could see them both through the partially frosted glass wall of Ashley's office, and she watched with steadily growing interest as their discussion appeared to become heated. Ray looked flushed and deeply upset. His voice was getting louder, and he began to lean forward, arms waving. Ashley was looking equally red-faced, but resolute and tight lipped. She laced her fingers in front of her, leant forward and said a few deliberate words. Ray then sat back in his chair and smiled ruefully at the ceiling, before getting to his feet and heading for the door, looking defeated.

"I might have known you'd be here," he growled at Katie as he brushed past her.

A few minutes later Ashley's PA ushered a nervous Katie into Ashley's office.

"Katie," said Ashley greeting her with a smile. "Good to see you. Just the person I wanted to speak to. Take a seat. We have a lot to discuss."

What Katie Did Next

"I don't see how it's going to work," said a voice from the back of the room. Katie peered around a few heads in the audience to see who was speaking. It wasn't the first time since becoming ROD that she had faced scepticism about the changes planned for the region.

It was almost a month since she had met with Ashley Cook intending to resign her role with Community Housing only to be offered the job of ROD, as Ray Briggs had been "redeployed to the South-East region to sort out a crisis."

"Eric lacked the drive and decisiveness to handle change," Ashley had said to Katie. "Ray went to the opposite extreme and people lost confidence in him. We believe you can find a happy medium between your predecessors. I realise it's a big step up, but I will be there to coach and support you through the process. I blame myself for not working more closely with Ray, but he doesn't take advice too well."

Now, as Katie faced another tricky question about the changes she was instigating, she called to mind her mentor's words.

"When people ask questions, it means they are trying to build a picture of the future. When the pieces of the puzzle don't seem to fit, they can get frustrated and seem hostile. But you should see the interrogation as a necessary part of the process. People

need to rearrange the furniture in their heads. It feels awkward. Everything's in the wrong place. That's why I call it 'Crazy Time'."

"I have to admit that I wasn't at all sure myself when I first heard about the job role changes," said Katie evenly, "and it took me a while to get my head around them. Which bits don't work for you, Derek?"

"Well, to be honest, I think the whole thing's confusing for our clients. They're used to workin' with us how we are now. They have their Housing Officer and sometimes they've known them for donkey's years. Putting in new faces will confuse them," said Derek Clark, one of the branch office Deputy Managers, from his seat at the back of the room.

The proposed job changes aimed to break down barriers between the different functions in Community Housing. Currently, problems were passed from department to department, leading to delays and issues getting lost in the system. Under the new structure, Housing Officers would be trained to take on a wider range of issues. They would serve fewer clients, but provide a more efficient and seamless service. Some staff members who had performed back office functions would now work with clients face-to-face. It meant people would need to be trained in a range of new skills, but the payoff in terms of improved service and greater efficiency made the time and effort worthwhile. The model had proven successful in a pilot region and was now being implemented nationwide.

"Do you know what kills change faster than anything?" Ashley had asked Katie. "Uncertainty," said Ashley, answering her own question. "Nature abhors a vacuum, but the devil loves one. Leave people in limbo, devoid of information and what do they do? They dream up all kinds of conspiracies and dreadful plans that deprive them of money, status or jobs." Katie knew this from bitter experience of Ray's brief reign as ROD. The region had been rife with rumours of the terrible plans he had in store for them.

People had gone off sick with stress, Katie had had nightmares and found herself about to quit the job she loved.

Katie was determined that this would not happen on her watch, which was why she was spending most of her time travelling around the region, working through her plans with people. "The best antidote for uncertainty is conversation," Ashley had advised her, "open, honest conversation. Remember, even bad news increases certainty, and it's better than no news at all, so keep the dialogue going. It can be a hard slog, but people change slowly. You need to build a wall of certainty brick by brick."

"I'll return to roles in a moment," continued Katie, "and you'll have plenty of time to work through the details during the rest of today. But first, let me remind you all once again of the purpose of these changes. We are on a mission to do what we all joined Community Housing to do – to provide decent housing to the poor and vulnerable – increasing employment prospects for adults and improving the life chances of children. These changes will allow us to deliver a service we can all be proud of while giving taxpayers value for money."

"Now, let's look at the changes in detail and the support people will get as they take on new responsibilities..."

"Setting a clear direction and sticking to it is a cornerstone of building certainty," Ashley had advised. "In times of difficulty and change, people look to their leaders for direction and confidence." Remembering Eric's constant indecision, Katie knew exactly what Ashley meant. "It all begins with you. Get yourself certain in your own mind about where you are going and what needs to be done. If you fail to do that, people will sense your uncertainty the moment you open your mouth. Remember, they're looking for someone they can trust to lead them out of the woods."

"We have full schedule today," continued Katie once she had briefly introduced the rationale behind the planned changes. "You're going to spend the rest of today working together to figure out for yourselves what the changes mean and how you can make them work with your own teams."

Later that day, as the workshop drew to a close, Katie was pleased to see the energy and enthusiasm that had developed as people began the mental journey from scepticism and doubt to understanding and belief. Not everyone was a raving fan of the changes, but it was dawning on most of them that the new job roles not only made sense, but provided a great opportunity to eliminate a lot of the problems that had dogged them in recent years. They knew the road would not be easy, but they had a plan they believed in and the support they needed to get people ready to take on new tasks.

"Ultimately, these changes will succeed or fail, not as a result of what I do or what anyone in Regional Head Office does, for that matter," said Katie. "As you all know, it's down to each of you to make it work in your offices."

"I do get it now," said Derek Clark, "it all makes sense to me, but our people struggle with change big time."

"I agree," replied Katie. "People do struggle with change, but they've managed it in the past and they'll manage it again with your help. The good news is you are already part way there. You already understand what needs to happen and why. It's almost impossible to support and sustain your team on the difficult journey of change unless you have a strong sense of purpose. Once you have that belief, you can begin building a wall of certainty brick by brick. And don't forget that I'll be on hand to support you through the process."

"Before we finish, let me introduce you to some more ideas about how to lead your people safely through Crazy Time..."

CONCLUSION:
THE 5 FORCES OF CHANGE

These five tales illustrate why people and organisations around the world struggle with change, and what can be done about it. For organisations to achieve successful change, their leaders should follow the examples of Bill, Cliff, George, Ravi and Katie to help their people become more purposeful, more in control of change, better able to shed the past, better equipped to succeed and more certain about the future as they get to grips with a new working environment. They will be well rewarded for their pains when people mobilise in support of change rather than avoiding or opposing it.

For a deeper understanding of these vital forces of change and for practical advice on how to achieve successful change in your organisation, read *The 5 Forces of Change: a blueprint for leading successful change* by Anthony Greenfield.

The
5 Forces of Change

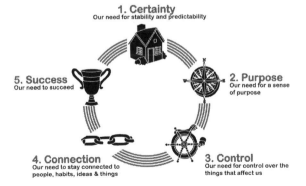

For further information see *www.5forcesofchange.com* or *www.mb2000.com,* or contact Anthony direct for training or direct support at: *info@5forcesofchange.com.*